SEARCH & FIND®

THE ADVENTURES OF TOM SAWYER

by
Mark Twain

Adapted by Chris Park
Illustrated by Tony Tallarico

A Kidsbooks® CLASSIC

Huckleberry Finn

Tom Sawyer

Becky Thatcher

Joe Harper

Injun Joe

Aunt Polly

TABLE of CONTENTS

CHAPTER ONE

Aunt Polly's Fence

Mark Twain's story about a boy named Tom Sawyer is based on his own adventures growing up in a small Missouri town in the 1800s. The story opens on a typical day, with Tom getting into trouble. His strict Aunt Polly, who is raising him along with his cousin Mary and his half-brother Sid, picks the perfect punishment. At least, she thinks it's perfect.

SEARCH & FIND®

Buckets (3)
Candles (2)
Artist's brush
Fishhooks (6)
Arrow
Butterfly
Horseshoes (2)
Flower
Knothole
Frog
Birds (2)
Knife
Coffeepot
Kites (2)
Spoon
Pie
Apples (4)
Heart
Mushroom
Pencil

In the morning, Tom ate up Aunt Polly's special jam, which was forbidden.

He ran away before Aunt Polly could punish him. Then he skipped school to go swimming.

After supper he got into a fight.

I CAN LICK YOU, ALFRED TEMPLE!

CAN!

NO YOU CAN'T!

CAN'T!

By the end of the day, Aunt Polly was determined to punish him in a way he wouldn't forget.

I'LL MAKE HIM WHITEWASH THE FENCE TOMORROW. TOM HATES WORK—ESPECIALLY ON SATURDAY.

CHAPTER TWO

Tom Falls in Love

om's trick paid off. Soon he had an armful of treasures, and the fence had three coats of whitewash. Aunt Polly could hardly believe her eyes.

SEARCH & FIND®

Chalk (4)

Bees (2)

Envelopes (2)

Pencil

Bottle

Beavers (2)

Snake

Mousehole

Heart

Top hats (2)

Owl

Lost sock

Snail

Hammer

Squirrels (2)

Skunk

Bows (10)

Rat

Turtle

Fish

I DECLARE! YOU DO WORK WHEN YOU WANT TO, TOM! ALL RIGHT, GO ON AND PLAY!

Tom ran down the alley to play soldiers with his friend Joe Harper. On his way home he saw a new girl at the Thatcher family's house.

SHE'S AS PRETTY AS AN ANGEL!

Tom forgot all about his girlfriend, Amy Lawrence. He did tricks to show off for the new girl.

The girl never spoke to him, but she threw him a flower.

CHAPTER THREE

Tom's Engagement

For once, Tom was happy to be punished. The girl seemed to ignore him at first, but when he drew some pictures, she became curious. She told him her name was Becky Thatcher. Tom fell more in love by the minute.

SEARCH & FIND®

CHAPTER FOUR

Murder at the Graveyard

Soon Joe Harper joined Tom to play in the woods, and Tom felt a bit better. But he was still hurt by Becky's rejection. That night he had just fallen asleep in the bed he shared with Sid when a noise woke him.

CHAPTER FIVE

Injun Joe's Big Lie

Speechless with horror, Huck and Tom dropped the dead cat and ran from the graveyard. They ducked inside an abandoned factory near town.

SEARCH & FIND®

Pick axe
Fish (2)
Envelopes (2)
Broken heart
Brooms (2)
Stars (2)
Kite
Barrels (2)
Shovel
Candle
Apple core
Rabbit
Tepee
Anchor
Oar
Knives (3)
Bucket
Rat
Bird
Snake

The boys pricked their thumbs and signed their initials in blood. Huck was burying the piece of wood they used for their note when they heard a howl. Tom looked out the window.

Tom and Huck heard another noise. It sounded like someone snoring loudly and it was coming from the attached shed.

Sid told Aunt Polly that Tom had snuck out, which made her very upset. At school, Tom and Joe Harper were punished for leaving school the day before. Then something worse happened.

Tom didn't have much time to think about Becky. By noon the whole town knew that Dr. Robinson had been killed. School was closed. Everyone headed for the graveyard.

CHAPTER SIX

Running Away

The sheriff put Muff in jail to await trial for murder. Tom and Huck wanted to tell the truth, but they were too scared of Injun Joe. Tom had nightmares for weeks.

Tom picked pirate names for everyone. They agreed to meet at a certain spot at the river that night. They chose a secret password.

WHO GOES THERE?

TOM SAWYER, THE BLACK AVENGER! NAME YOUR NAMES!

HUCK FINN, THE RED-HANDED.

JOE HARPER, THE TERROR OF THE SEAS.

SAY THE SECRET PASSWORD!

BLOOD!

PUSH OFF, MATES!

AYE, AYE, CAPTAIN!

The town lay sleeping next to them as the boys headed down the river. Tom knew he might never see his family or his other friends again. He was too excited to care, even about Becky.

CHAPTER SEVEN

Pirates on Jackson's Island

The boys steered their raft down the dark river for hours. Finally the raft scraped up against a sandbar. They jumped off onto Jackson's Island.

SEARCH & FIND®

CHAPTER EIGHT

Tom Sneaks Back Home

At first the boys were excited and happy that people were searching for them. It made them feel important. But for one of them, the good mood didn't last long.

SEARCH & FIND®

Ear of corn
Cupcake
Hammer
Umbrellas (2)
Fishhooks (2)
Pencil
Whale
Carrot
Driftwood (2)
Tepee
Rings (3)
Lost hat
Snail
Top hat
Feather
Cups (2)
Wagon wheel
Bottle
Five-pointed stars (3)
Worm

CHAPTER NINE

What Tom Heard

When the ferry docked, Tom slipped out of the rowboat and ran home. A light was shining in the sitting room where Aunt Polly usually slept. Mrs. Harper, Mary, and Sid were there, too.

SEARCH & FIND

Oar

Drum

Butterfly

Brooms (2)

Ring

Fish

Pencils (2)

Feathers (2)

Bat

Paintbrush

Keys (2)

Cup

Slingshot

Mouse

Sailboat

Spoons (2)

Broken heart

Toothbrush

Tomahawks (2)

Forks (3)

Panel 1 (speech bubbles):

THAT'S WHAT MUST HAVE HAPPENED. THEY FOUND THE EMPTY RAFT, AND THE SEARCH BOATS LOOKED EVERYWHERE.

THE MINISTER SAYS IF THEY DON'T TURN UP BY SATURDAY, HE'LL HAVE THE FUNERAL ON SUNDAY.

MAYBE TOM WON'T GO TO HEAVEN. HE WAS BAD SOMETIMES.

SID!

Panel 2:

Aunt Polly scolded Sid for saying anything bad about Tom. Mrs. Harper left, and Sid and Mary went to bed. Aunt Polly lay in her own bed.

MY POOR BOY!

Panel 3:

Tom sniffled back some tears. He was sorry Aunt Polly was so sad. When her steady breathing told him she was asleep, he pulled out the note.

We are not dead. We are only off being pirates.

Panel 4:

Tom was about to put the note on the bedside table . . .

We are not dead. We are only off being pirates.

Panel 5:

But then he decided not to leave it after all. He had an idea for a wonderful new plan.

CHAPTER TEN

Tom's Secret

om walked back to the ferryboat. Since it was still hours before dawn, only a few workers were around. He untied the rowboat and began his trip back.

SEARCH & FIND®

Locomotive
Kite
Horseshoe
Open can
Mice (2)
Mushroom
Egg
Raccoons (2)
Turtles (2)
Bat
Mule
Oil lamp
Owl
Barrel
Rabbit
Frying pan
Apples (3)
Suns (2)
Fish (3)
Slingshots (2)

CHAPTER ELEVEN

"It's a Miracle!"

The boys played extra hard the next couple of days. They were excited by their plan, and they knew their pirate days were almost over. The last night brought a huge storm.

SEARCH & FIND®

Snakes (2)
Cup
Candles (2)
Heart
Books (2)
Artist's brush
Bucket
Slingshot
Arrow
Spoon
Oars (2)
Music notes (3)
Bat
Ring
Turtle
Drums (2)
Apple
Birds (2)
Stars (2)
Umbrella

CHAPTER TWELVE

Tom's Fantastic "Dream"

 unt Polly was so happy Tom was safe she didn't punish him for running away. But by Monday morning, she was starting to scold. That's when Tom added something new to his story.

SEARCH & FIND®

Kettles (2)

Fork

Owls (2)

Scissors

Kite

Chest

Feather

Skull and crossbones

Oil lamp

Heart

Quarter moon

Stars (2)

Boat

Sword

Lightning bolt

Slingshots (2)

Telescopes (2)

Bows (5)

Hammer

Top hat

YOU CERTAINLY MADE ME SUFFER, TOM. DIDN'T YOU CARE ENOUGH TO SEND ME A MESSAGE THAT YOU WERE SAFE?

I'M SURE TOM WOULD HAVE TOLD US IF HE COULD.

I DO CARE ABOUT YOU, AUNT POLLY! WHY, I EVEN HAD A DREAM ABOUT YOU WEDNESDAY NIGHT.

Tom knew Aunt Polly believed in dreams and lucky charms. She was superstitious.

WHAT KIND OF DREAM?

I DREAMED YOU WERE IN THE SITTING ROOM. MRS. HARPER WAS HERE, TOO. AND SID AND MARY. EVERYONE LOOKED SAD. WELL, EXCEPT SID.

WHY, SO WE WERE! WHAT ELSE?

YOU SAID I WASN'T BAD—JUST IRRESPONSIBLE AS A PUPPY.

MERCY! THEN WHAT?

YOU SAID I WAS GENEROUS AND SMART. THEN THERE WAS TALK OF HAVING THE FUNERAL ON SUNDAY.

AS I LIVE AND BREATHE!

I LEFT A MESSAGE BY YOUR BED WHEN YOU WERE ASLEEP. IT SAID: "WE ARE NOT DEAD. WE ARE ONLY OFF BEING PIRATES."

SO YOU DID THINK OF ME AFTER ALL, TOM! HERE'S SOMETHING FOR A GOOD BOY.

At school, kids made a big fuss over Tom and Joe. The two boys made their adventures sound especially exciting.

THE LIGHTNING SMASHED INTO THE ROCKS RIGHT WHERE WE WERE SITTING!

WE ALMOST GOT KILLED!

Tom got stuck-up from the attention. He decided to ignore Becky the way she had ignored him. But she found a way to get even.

THAT FANCY-PANTS ALFRED TEMPLE! I SHOULD WHIP HIM AGAIN!

When Tom came home at lunchtime, Aunt Polly met him at the door. She was furious.

TOM SAWYER, I SHOULD SKIN YOU ALIVE!

WHAT DID I DO?

I TOLD MRS. HARPER THAT NONSENSE ABOUT YOUR DREAM. BUT JOE HAD ALREADY TOLD HER THE TRUTH—THAT YOU SNUCK BACK AND OVERHEARD US. YOU MADE ME LOOK LIKE A FOOL!

Tom was ashamed. He had thought it would be a good joke to make up the dream. Now it seemed mean.

I'M SORRY, AUNT POLLY. BUT I REALLY DID WRITE YOU A MESSAGE!

IT'S THE TRUTH!

TOM, I CAN'T STAND ANY MORE OF YOUR LIES!

That night Aunt Polly looked in the pocket of Tom's pirating jacket.

BLESS HIS HEART! I CAN FORGIVE A THOUSAND TRICKS FOR THIS SWEET MESSAGE.

CHAPTER THIRTEEN

The Trial of Muff Potter

Summer vacation started, and Tom got the measles. He wanted to scratch, but Aunt Polly warned he'd have scars. When he was well, Muff Potter's trial was beginning.

SEARCH & FIND®

Huck and Tom visited Muff to cheer him up.

Muff's gratitude made Huck and Tom feel even guiltier. Finally . . .

CHAPTER FOURTEEN

Hunting for Treasure

Tom was treated as a hero for telling the truth. He liked the fuss and was happy Muff was free. But he was also afraid—especially at night.

SEARCH & FIND®

Tom imagined Injun Joe hiding everywhere, waiting to attack.

After awhile Tom relaxed. He and Huck decided to search for buried treasure, since they hadn't found any on Jackson's Island.

HOW DO YOU RECKON THIS IS A GOOD PLACE TO DIG, TOM?

BECAUSE IN PIRATE BOOKS, LOTS OF TIMES TREASURE IS BURIED UNDER A DEAD TREE WITH ONE LIMB STICKING OUT. YOU DIG WHERE THE LIMB'S SHADOW FALLS.

They dug and dug, but found only rocks.

LOOKS LIKE WE PICKED THE WRONG PLACE, TOM.

WAIT A MINUTE! IN THE PIRATE BOOKS, THEY DIG WHERE THE SHADOW FALLS AT MIDNIGHT! WE'LL HAVE TO COME BACK.

Huck came by Tom's house that night and gave the signal.

MEOW!

CHAPTER FIFTEEN

In the Haunted House

 he boys tiptoed around the first floor. Then they tossed their pick and shovel in a corner and climbed the rickety staircase. A spike of fear shot through Tom as he heard a noise below.

SEARCH & FIND®

Padlock
Fish (2)
Candles (2)
Pencil
Bell
Bats (2)
Worms (2)
Mouse
Keys (2)
Jack-o'-lantern
Oil lamp
Paintbrush
Ice pick
Moths (2)
Skull
Bow
Arrow
Rings (2)
Spiderweb
Turtle

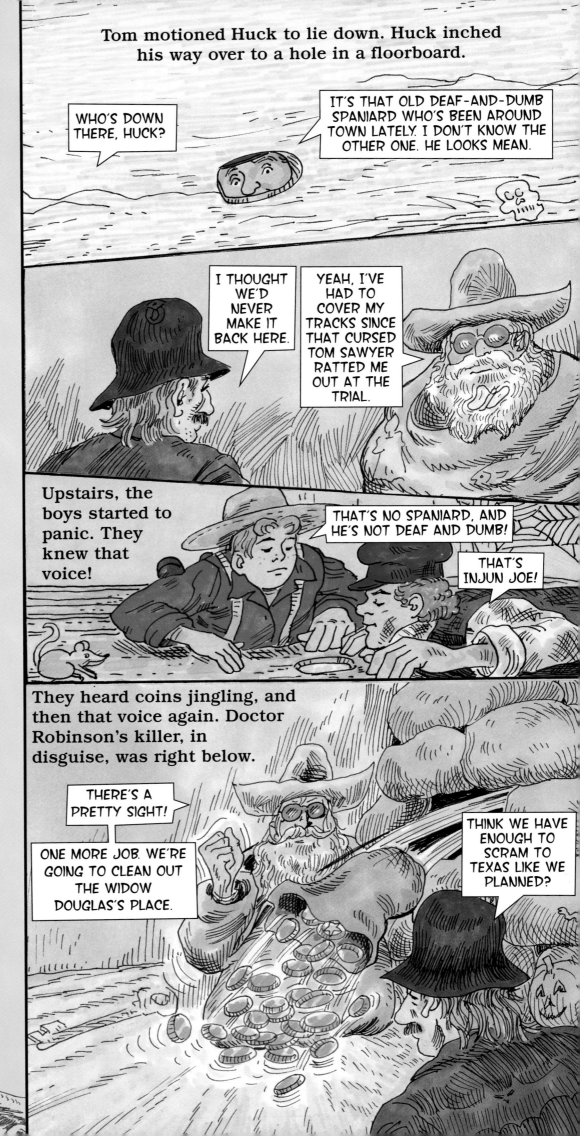

CHAPTER SIXTEEN

Missing!

Tom and Huck waited until it was safe to climb out a window and run away. They agreed to search for Den Number Two around town. Tom's class was having a picnic the next day. Huck said he would watch for the robbers around Widow Douglas's house.

SEARCH & FIND®

Gravestones (2)

Becky's blue ribbons (4)

Cupcakes (2)

Scissors

Fish (2)

Hearts (2)

Horseshoes (2)

Kites (2)

Stars (2)

Snakes (2)

Bottles (2)

Coffeepot

Quarter moons (2)

Padlocks (2)

Lanterns (8)

Knives (2)

Pencils (2)

Top hats (2)

Apples (2)

Bell

IF THEY SHOW UP, I'LL GO GET MR. JONES. HE AND HIS BOYS LIVE ON CARDIFF HILL, DOWN FROM THE WIDOW.

ALL RIGHT. I'LL COME FIND YOU WHEN I GET BACK FROM THE PICNIC.

Tom's classmates were going to McDougal's Cave. It was a huge cave in the rocky bluffs above the river. Parents weren't coming. Teenagers would look out for the younger children. Tom and Becky had made up, and now he couldn't wait to see her.

WHAT DID YOU BRING FOR LUNCH?

BEHAVE YOURSELF!

I HEARD THERE ARE MILLIONS OF BATS INSIDE!

SPIDERS, TOO!

REST AFTER YOU EAT!

The boat would not return until late. Some children planned to stay overnight with friends who lived near the dock.

I'LL ASK JOE OR BEN IF I CAN SLEEP OVER.

FINE WITH ME!

I'LL ASK SUSY HARPER IF I CAN STAY WITH HER.

ALL RIGHT, DEAR. WE'LL MEET YOU AT CHURCH TOMORROW.

CHAPTER SEVENTEEN

Lost in the Cave

Meanwhile, Tom and Becky had spent four days and four nights in the gigantic cave, with practically no food or water. What began as a game became an ordeal.

SEARCH & FIND®

Burnt-out candle
Pencil
Feather
Flowers (2)
Bones (2)
Black cat
Ring
Hammer
Envelope
Top hats (3)
Umbrella
Music notes (2)
Drum
Artist's brush
Shovels (2)
Arrow
Fish
Kites (2)
Key
Bird

The Treasure at Last!

T he fishermen who found them brought the weak, tired children home. They were put to bed to recover. Huck was sick in bed, too. He had caught a fever from being outside in the cold, watching for the robbers.

SEARCH & FIND®

Tomahawks (2)

Heart

Candles (5)

Lost boot

Quarter moons (3)

Ring

Hammer

Carrots (2)

Bird

Umbrella

Artist's brush

Star

Horseshoe

Snake

Cupcakes (2)

Kite

Fish (2)

Toothbrush

Bat

Skulls (2)

BUT TOM, MCDOUGAL'S CAVE IS ALL SHUT UP! JUDGE THATCHER HAD A BIG IRON DOOR PUT ON AFTER YOU TWO WERE FOUND. HE'S GOT THE KEYS.

THAT WAS TWO WEEKS AGO. INJUN JOE MAY STILL BE INSIDE!

The boys ran to tell Judge Thatcher. The judge got the sheriff. Soon the enormous metal door stood open. There lay Injun Joe with a broken knife at his side.

POOR DEVIL!

HE MUST HAVE STARVED TO DEATH TRYING TO DIG UNDER THE DOOR.

Tom and Huck were sorry Injun Joe died that way. At the same time, they felt safer. They knew the other robber's body had been found in the river. Now the treasure was unprotected.

ARE YOU SURE YOU MARKED THE PLACE WHERE YOU AND BECKY GOT OUT?

YEP. THE HOLE IS NEAR THAT WHITE PATCH WHERE THERE'S BEEN A LANDSLIDE. SOMEDAY WE'LL HAVE A ROBBER'S GANG AND USE THIS PLACE AS A HIDEOUT, HUCK!

In the cave, Tom found the X easily. The boys explored several passages, then came back to lean against a big rock and think. Tom jumped up.

I'LL BET IT'S UNDER THIS ROCK!

LET'S DIG!

Soon their shovel struck wooden boards. The boards were covering up the entrance to a lower room. And in that room, finally . . .

THERE MUST BE FIFTY POUNDS OF GOLD HERE!

TOM, WE'RE RICH!

CHAPTER NINETEEN

Huckleberry Finn's New Life

They poured the heavy gold into small bags and carried the bags to the boat. Back in town, they borrowed a small wagon to haul their loot up Cardiff Hill. They planned to count their money in the Widow Douglas's woodshed. Mr. Jones stopped them.

SEARCH & FIND®

Pears (3)

Chicken

Hearts (2)

Gavel

Bells (2)

Knife

Horseshoe

Stars (2)

Flowers (2)

Open can

Toothbrush

Screwdriver

Mice (3)

Umbrella

Padlock

Pencils (2)

Fishhooks (2)

Fish

Frog

Kite

I WILL SPEND ALL THE MONEY IT TAKES TO GET YOU A GOOD EDUCATION. THEN I'LL HELP YOU START YOUR OWN BUSINESS.

WHAT GOOD LUCK FOR HUCKLEBERRY, POOR THING.

HE'S NOT POOR! HE'S RICH, AND I CAN PROVE IT!

Tom ran outside and came back dragging several bags.

THERE! SEE? HALF OF IT BELONGS TO HUCK AND HALF BELONGS TO ME!

MERCY, I'VE NEVER SEEN SO MUCH MONEY!

NEITHER HAVE I!

NEITHER HAVE I!

The boys' gold was put into the bank. Huck's adoption went through as planned. He needed a grown-up to help him manage all that money. But one day . . .

HUCKLEBERRY'S BEEN MISSING FOR TWO DAYS! THE WIDOW IS FRANTIC! TOM, CAN YOU GO LOOK FOR HIM?

Tom found Huck in an old shed by the river.

I'M NOT GOING BACK, TOM. I DON'T WANT TO LIVE IN A FANCY HOUSE AND GO TO SCHOOL.

BUT WHAT ABOUT OUR ROBBERS' GANG?

IT WON'T BE FAIR TO THE WIDOW IF YOU DON'T GO BACK.

Luckily, Tom had an imagination. He used it to help his friend make the right choice.

I CAN'T LET YOU IN IF YOU'RE NOT RESPECTABLE.

ROBBERS ARE MORE HIGH-CLASS. AND THEY'VE ALL BEEN TO SCHOOL.

WHAT? YOU LET ME BE A PIRATE!

Huck promised to give the widow's place another try. Tom said he would ask the widow to relax some rules for Huck. They decided to have the initiation for the Tom Sawyer Gang that night in the graveyard.

WE'LL SWEAR NEVER TO TELL THE GANG'S SECRETS, EVEN IF WE GET CHOPPED TO PIECES.

A ROBBERS' GANG IS A MILLION TIMES BETTER THAN PIRATING!

The End

Quick Quiz

Check your answers on page 45.

1 Tom's parents are not in the story. Whom does he live with?

   a. his uncle

   b. his stepmother

   c. his aunt

   d. Huck's father

2 One of the first signs in the book that Tom has a great imagination is when he tricks his friends into doing a chore for him. What is that chore?

   a. cleaning his room

   b. building a fence

   c. painting a fence

   d. making lunch

3 Who is Tom's good friend, even though the townspeople do not approve?

   a. Huckleberry Finn   b. Joe Harper   c. Injun Joe   d. Becky Thatcher

4 Tom is imaginative and mischievous. Which of these words also describes him?

   a. cautious

   b. adventurous

   c. sad

   d. cold

5 In the graveyard, Tom and Huck hear voices. Whose voices are they?

   a. Injun Joe, Muff Potter, and Doctor Robinson

   b. Injun Joe alone

   c. Becky Thatcher and her father

   d. Aunt Polly and Judge Thatcher

6 Tom and Huck witness the murder of which man?

   a. Huck's father

   b. Injun Joe

   c. Muff Potter

   d. Doctor Robinson

7 Whom does the sheriff accuse of committing the murder?

   a. Huckleberry Finn

   b. Muff Potter

   c. Doctor Robinson

   d. Aunt Polly

8 After learning that people think he is dead, Tom sneaks back to town. What is one of his reasons for doing so?

   a. He is sick.

   b. He feels proud.

   c. He feels guilty.

   d. He is cold.

9 Tom plans to leave a note for Aunt Polly telling her that he is alive. He changes his mind, though, and lets her go on thinking that he is dead. What is his reason for doing this?

   a. He wants to tell Aunt Polly in person.

   b. He wants to make Aunt Polly suffer.

   c. He wants to run away permanently.

   d. He wants to attend his own funeral.

10 At the haunted house, Tom and Huck overhear Injun Joe say that he is going to rob whose home?

   a. Aunt Polly's

   b. Judge Thatcher's

   c. Muff Potter's

   d. the Widow Douglas's

Activity Adventures

Extra, Extra—Read All About It!

Imagine you are a reporter for a newspaper in Tom's hometown. Create the front page of the newspaper, reporting stories that occur in the book. Which one would be the lead story? Here are some ideas to start you off:

- Tom, Joe, and Huck run away to Jackson's Island
- The murder of Doc Robinson
- Injun Joe's escape

What other events would be interesting to read about?

Mapping Tom Sawyer's World

Tom's adventures take him far and wide. On a separate piece of paper or poster board, draw a map of all the places Tom visits in this book. Start with Aunt Polly's house and remember to include the Mississippi River!

- Becky Thatcher's house
- Jackson's Island
- The haunted house
- The graveyard
- McDougal's cave
- Widow Douglas's house

Write a Letter to Mark Twain

If you were to write a letter to Mark Twain, what would you say? What questions would you ask? Here are a few suggestions to get you started:

- What did you like most about the story?
- Write about your favorite character, and tell why that person is your favorite.
- Would you change any part of Tom's adventure?

About the Author

Mark Twain

S amuel Langhorne Clemens was born in 1835 in Florida, Missouri. He left home in 1853 and tried several different careers.

In 1863, Clemens first used the name "Mark Twain" (a phrase used by crews on Mississippi river boats) as his signature on a humorous letter. Later he started using the name as a pen name, or pseudonym (SOO-do-nim). Little did he know how famous that pseudonym would become.

Clemens published his first novel-length book in 1869, and many others followed. The events recorded in *The Adventures of Tom Sawyer*, published in 1876, are said to be an accurate account of the author's own adventurous childhood antics.

Samuel Clemens died in 1910, leaving great gifts for the world and a name that will live on forever.